The Faber Music

EASY PIANO ANTHOLOGY

Best-loved pop, jazz, film, folk and classical pieces specially arranged for easy solo piano

FABER *ff* MUSIC

Cover image: Moonshine, 1919 (gouache & w/c on linen), Klee, Paul (1879–1940)
Private Collection / Photo © Christie's Images / Bridgeman Images

Designed by Kenosha Design
New arrangements by Oliver Weeks & Lucy Holliday
Edited by Lucy Holliday

© 2020 by Faber Music Ltd
First published by Faber Music Ltd in 2020
Bloomsbury House
74–77 Great Russell Street
London WC1B 3DA

Printed and bound in Turkey by Imago
ISBN: 0-571-54121-6
EAN: 978-0-571-54121-8

To buy Faber Music publications or to find out about the full range of titles available,
please contact your local music retailer or Faber Music sales enquiries:

Faber Music Limited, Burnt Mill, Elizabeth Way, Harlow CM20 2HX
Tel: +44 (0)1279 82 89 82   Fax: +44 (0)1279 82 89 83
sales@fabermusic.com   fabermusicstore.com

Largo from 'New World Symphony'

Composed by Antonín Dvořák

Air On The G String

Composed by Johann Sebastian Bach

All Through The Night

Welsh Traditional

Can't Help Falling In Love

Words and Music by George David Weiss, Hugo Peretti and Luigi Creatore

I Vow To Thee, My Country

Composed by Gustav Holst

They Can't Take That Away From Me

Music and Lyrics by George Gershwin and Ira Gershwin

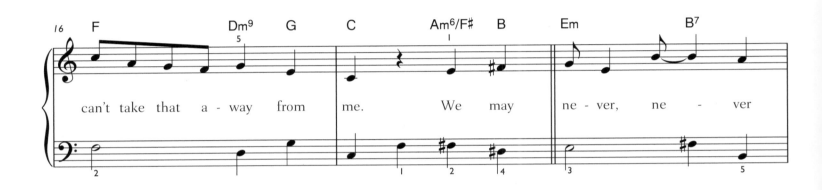

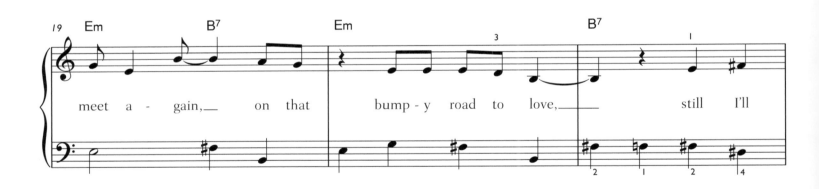

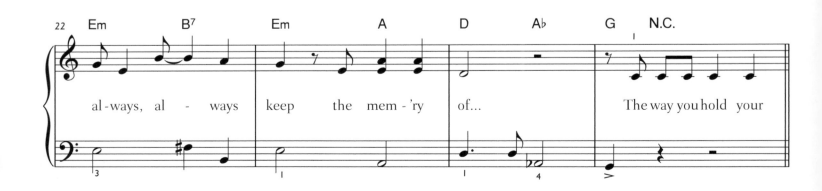

knife, the way we danced till three,

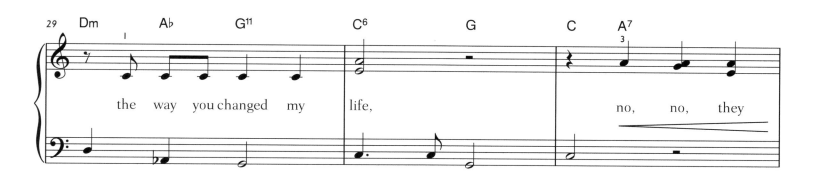

the way you changed my life, no, no, they

can't take that a-way from me, no, they can't take that a-

-way from me!

Ev'ry Time We Say Goodbye

Words and Music by Cole Porter

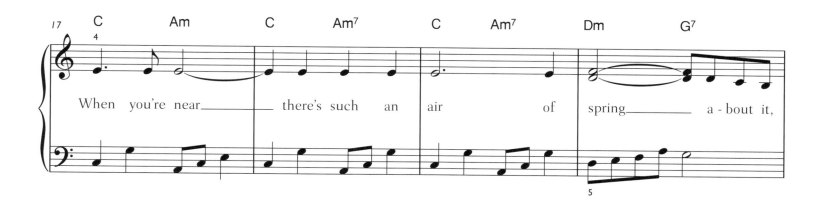

When you're near____ there's such an air of spring____ a-bout it,

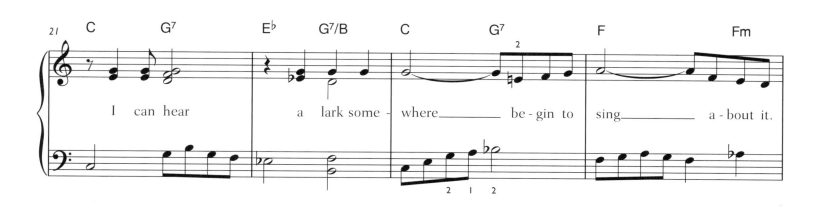

I can hear a lark some - where____ be-gin to sing____ a-bout it.

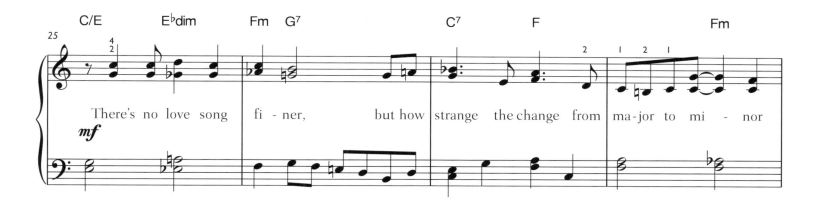

There's no love song fi - ner, but how strange the change from ma-jor to mi - nor

mf

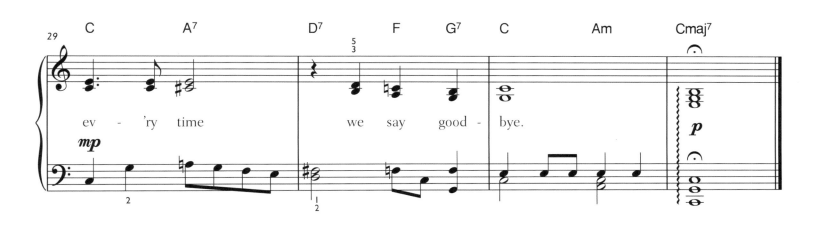

ev - 'ry time we say good - bye.

mp

p

Ave Maria

Composed by Franz Schubert

Imagine

Words and Music by John Lennon

1. Im - a - gine there's no hea - ven,
2. Im - a - gine there's no coun - tries,
3. Im - a - gine no pos - ses - sions,

it's ea - sy if you try.
it is - n't hard to do.
I won - der if you can.

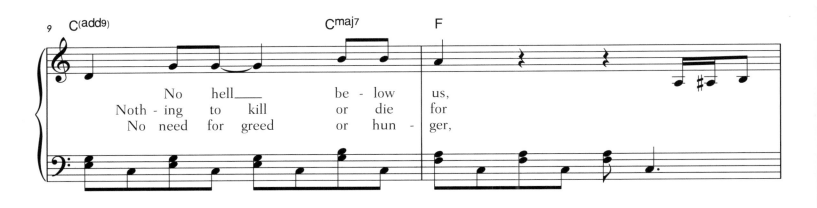

No hell____ be - low us,
Noth - ing to kill or die for
No need for greed or hun - ger,

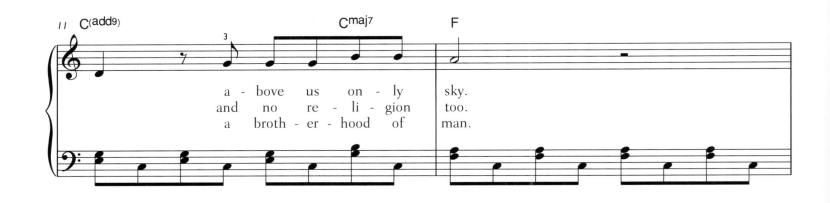

a - bove us on - ly sky.
and no re - li - gion too.
a broth - er - hood of man.

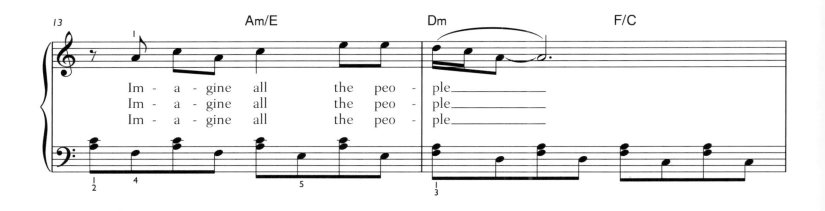

Im - a - gine all the peo - ple____
Im - a - gine all the peo - ple____
Im - a - gine all the peo - ple____

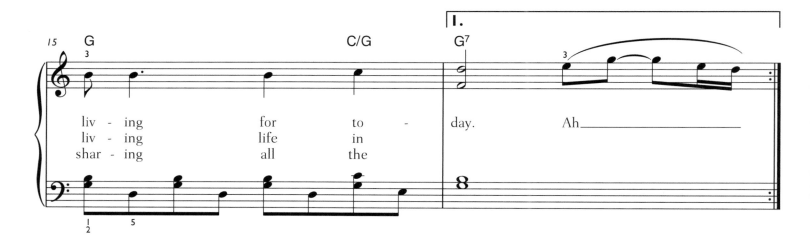

liv - ing for to - day. Ah____
liv - ing life in
shar - ing all the

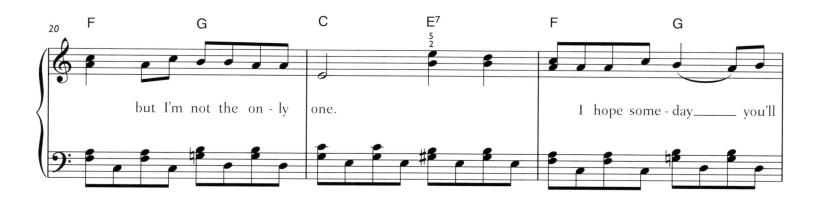

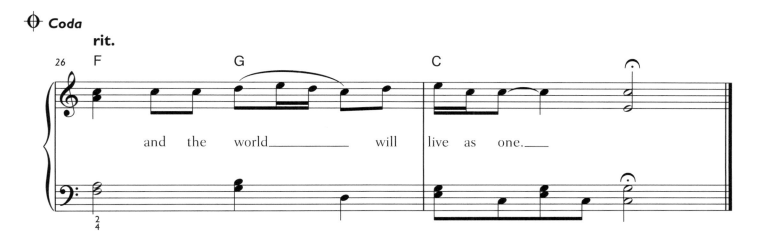

May It Be

(from *The Lord Of The Rings: The Fellowship Of The Ring*)

Words by Roma Ryan
Music by Enya and Nicky Ryan

far   you__ are   from   home._____
rise   to__ find   the   sun._____

Mor - ni -

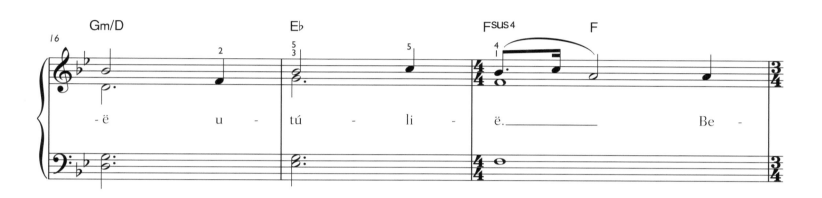

-ë   u - tú - li - ë._____   Be -

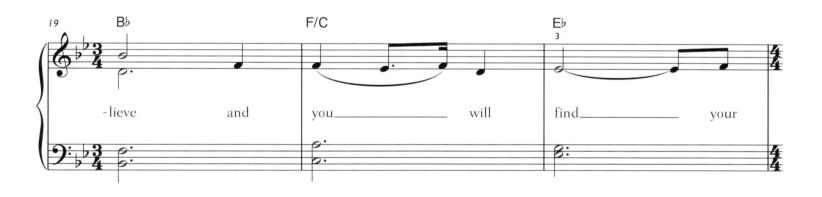

-lieve   and   you_____ will   find_____   your

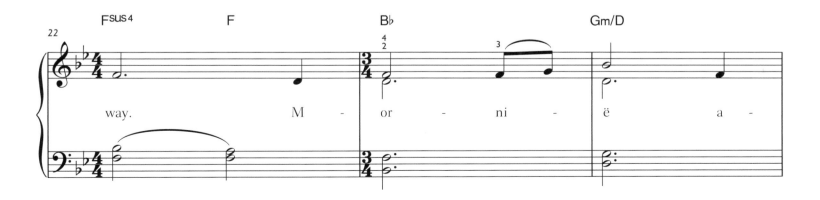

way.   M - or - ni - ë   a -

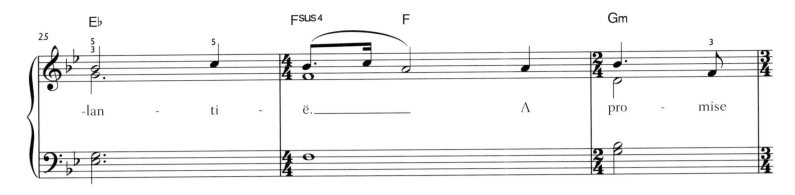

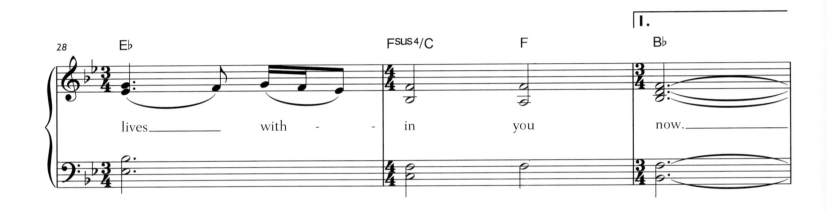

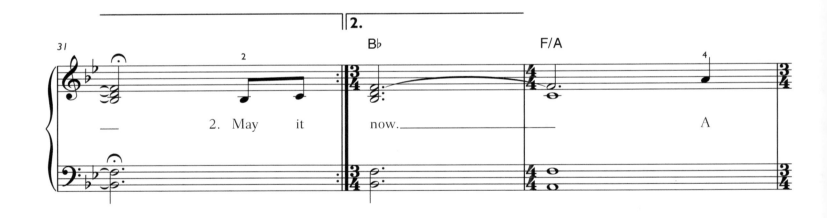

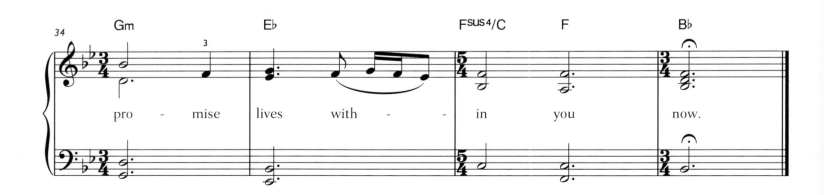

La Caroline

Composed by C.P.E. Bach

Is That Alright?

Words and Music by Stefani Germanotta, Nick Monson, Aaron Raitiere, Paul Blair, Mark Nilan and Lukas Nelson

10 C/E   Am

tryin' to fi - gure out_____ the world.
when you know___ I_____ need help.

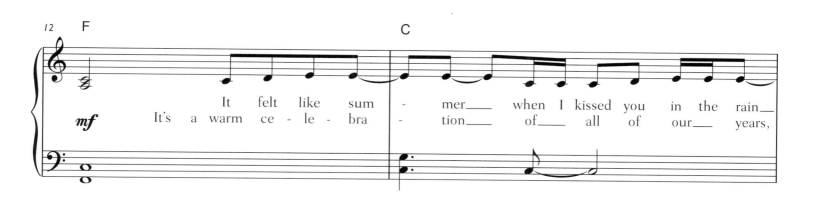

12 F   C

mf

It felt like sum - mer___ when I kissed you in the rain___
It's a warm ce - le - bra - tion___ of___ all of our___ years,

14 C/E   Am   F

___ and I know your sto - ry, but tell me a - gain.___
___ I dream of our sto - ry, of our fai - ry tale.___

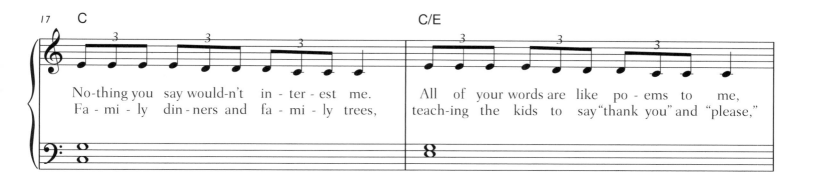

17 C   C/E

No-thing you say would-n't in - ter - est me. All of your words are like po - ems to me,
Fa - mi - ly din - ners and fa - mi - ly trees, teach-ing the kids to say "thank you" and "please,"

I would be hon-oured if you would take me as I am.
know - ing if we stay to - geth - er that things will be right.
I want

you
to look right in my eyes,

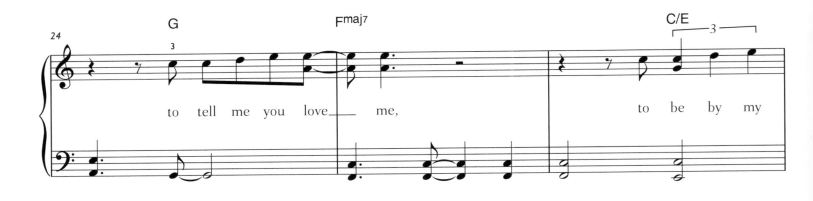

to tell me you love me,
to be by my

side.
I want you

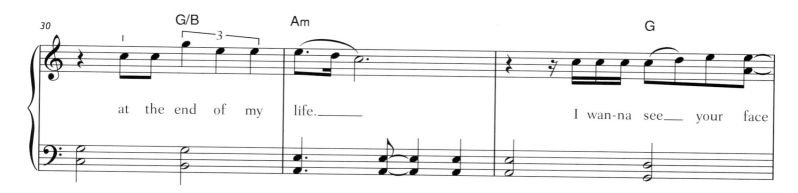

at the end of my life._____ I wan-na see___ your face

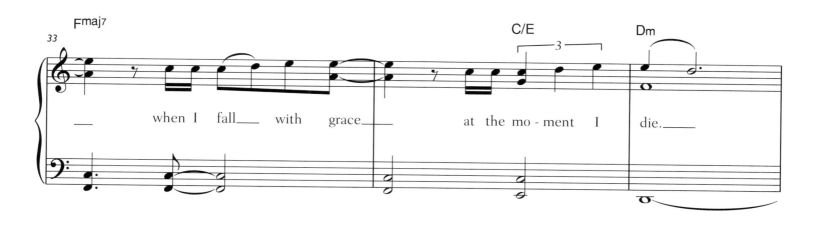

_____ when I fall___ with grace_____ at the mo - ment I die._____

Is that al - right? Is that al -

- right? Is_____ that_____ al - right?

Star Wars (Main Theme)

Composed by John Williams

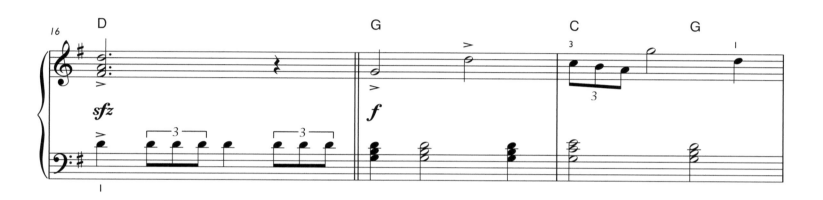

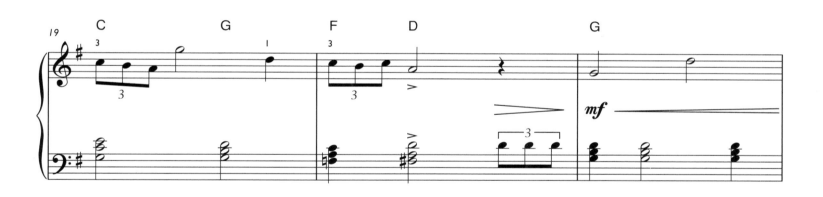

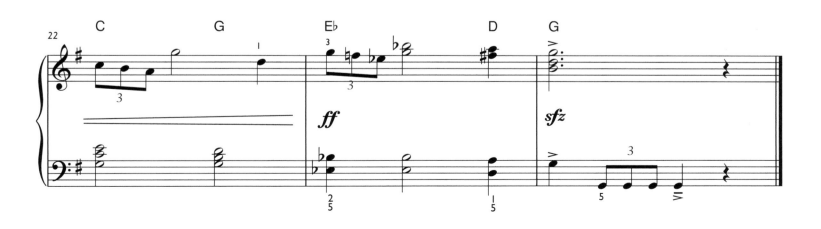

The Skye Boat Song

Words by Harold Boulton
Music, Traditional

Baff - led our foes stand by the shore, fol - low they will not

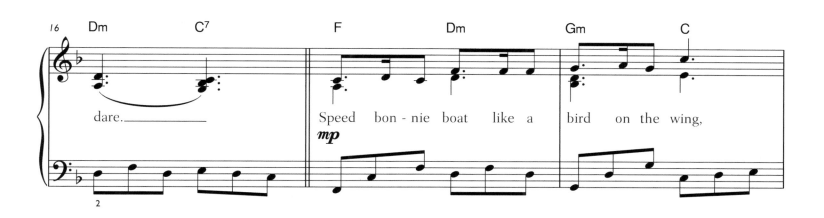

dare._____ Speed bon - nie boat like a bird on the wing,

mp

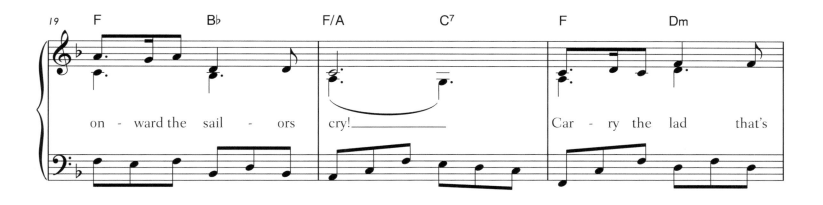

on - ward the sail - ors cry!_____ Car - ry the lad that's

Slower

born to be King ov - er the sea to Skye.

Greensleeves

Traditional

Scarborough Fair

Traditional

Eine Kleine Nachtmusik

Composed by Wolfgang Amadeus Mozart

On The Street Where You Live
(from *My Fair Lady*)

Words by Alan Jay Lerner
Music by Frederick Loewe

Moderately

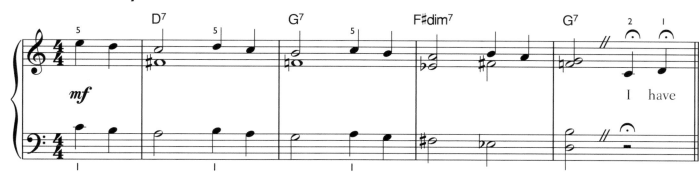

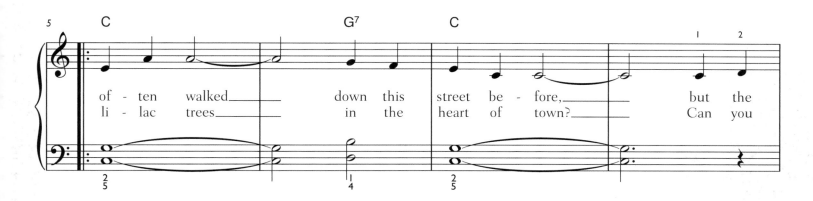

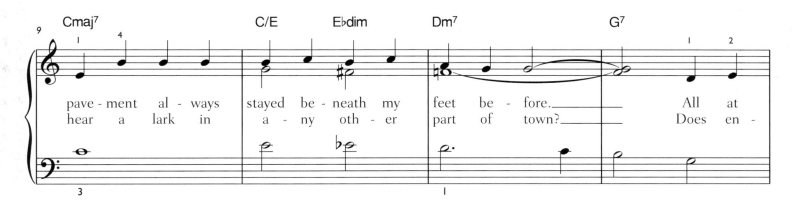

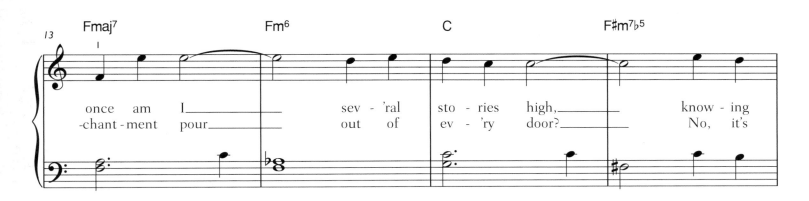

Over The Rainbow
(from *The Wizard Of Oz*)

Music by Harold Arlen
Lyrics by E.Y. "Yip" Harburg

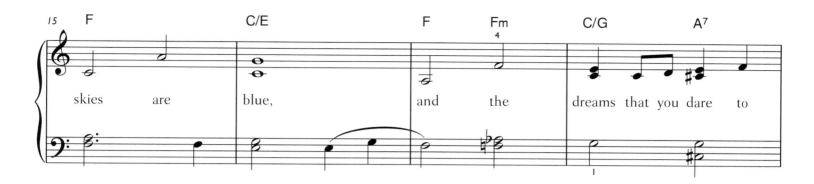

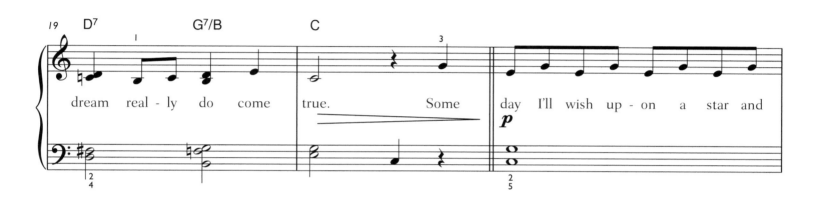

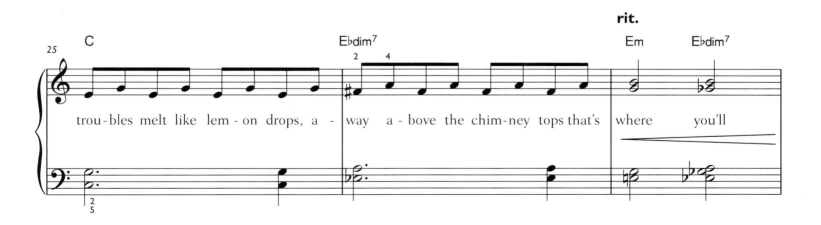

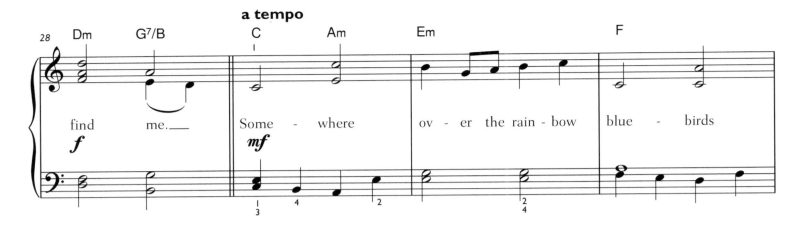

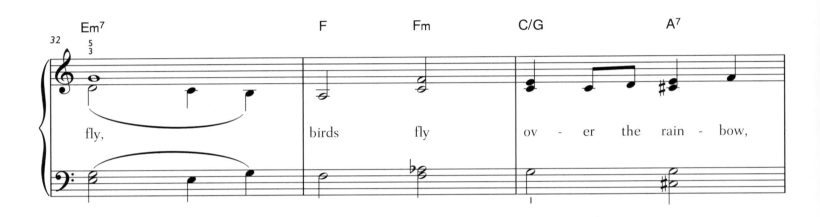

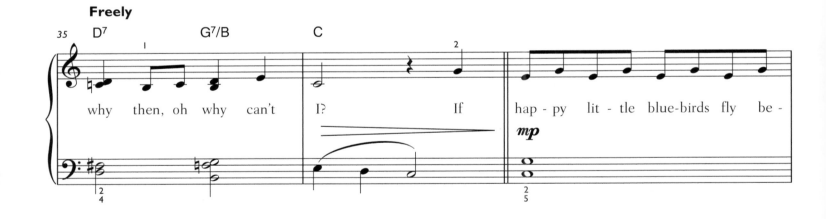

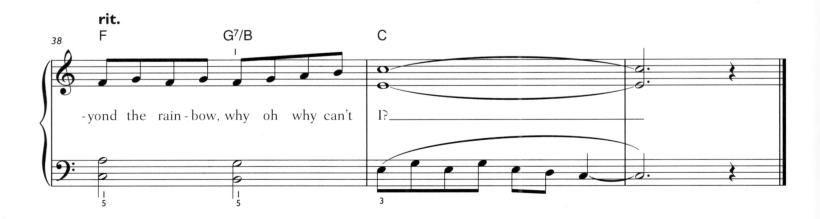

Memory
(from *Cats!*)

Music by Andrew Lloyd Webber
Text by Trevor Nunn after T. S. Eliot

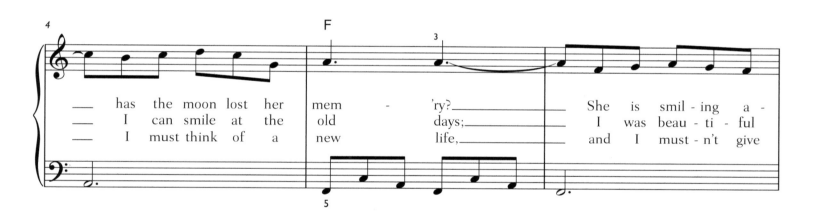

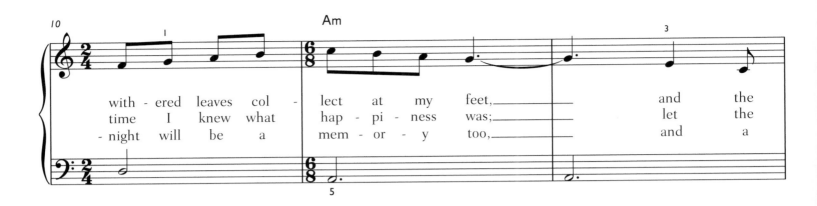

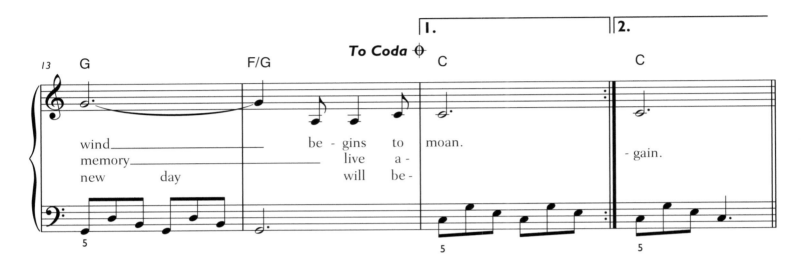

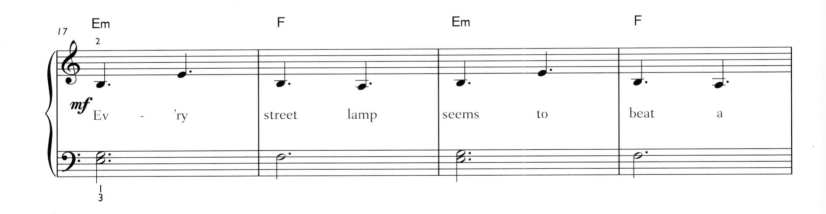

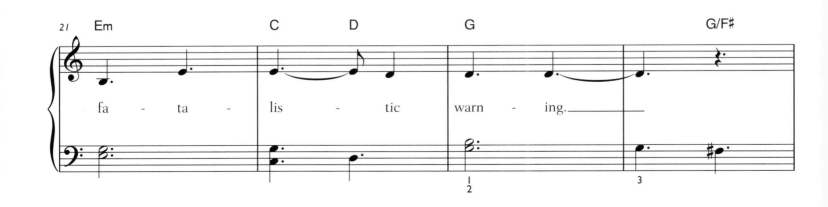

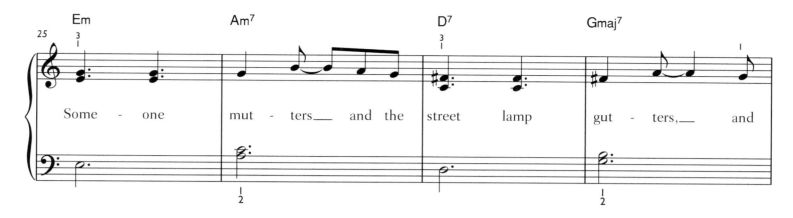

Some - one mut - ters___ and the street lamp gut - ters,___ and

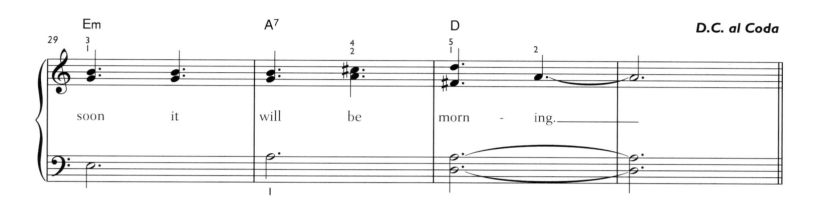

D.C. al Coda

soon it will be morn - ing.___

Coda

- gin.

p

rit.

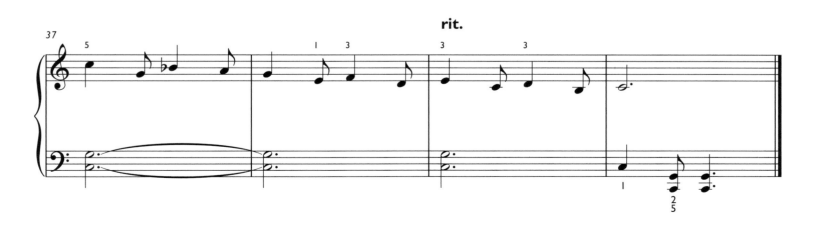

Cradle Song

Composed by Robert Schumann

Winter Wonderland

Words by Dick Smith
Music by Felix Bernard

The Rose

Words and Music by Amanda McBroom

The House Of The Rising Sun

Traditional

Moderately

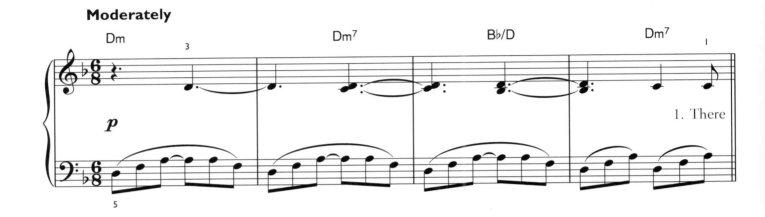

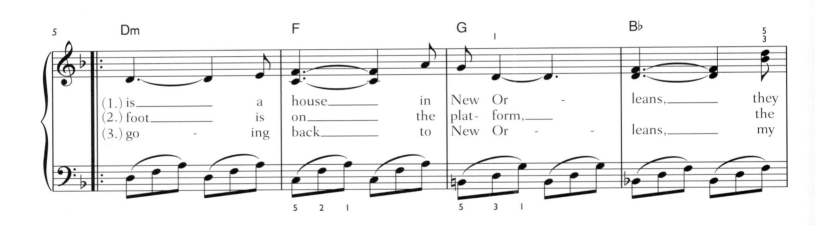

(1.) is ___ a house ___ in New Or - leans, ___ they
(2.) foot ___ is on ___ the plat- form, ___ the
(3.) go - ing back ___ to New Or - leans, ___ my

call ___ the Ris - ing ___ Sun, ___ it's
oth - er one on ___ the ___ train. ___ I'm
race ___ is al - most ___ run. ___

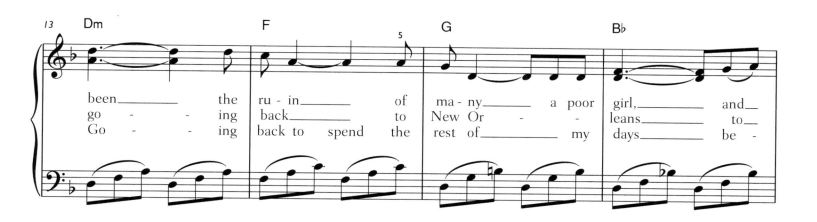

Slower

When I Fall In Love

Words by Edward Heyman
Music by Victor Young

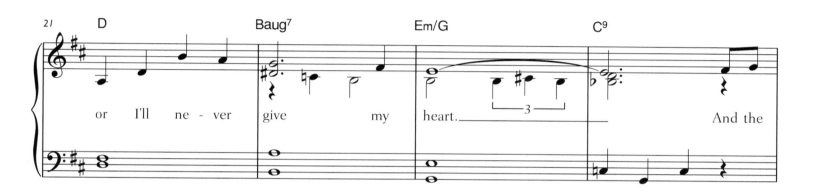

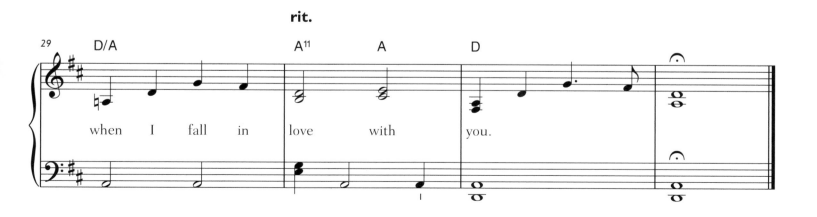

The Lord Is My Shepherd (Psalm 23)

Composed by Howard Goodall

Space Oddity

Words and Music by David Bowie

Chasing Cars

Words and Music by Gary Lightbody, Tom Simpson, Paul Wilson, Jonathan Quinn and Nathan Connolly

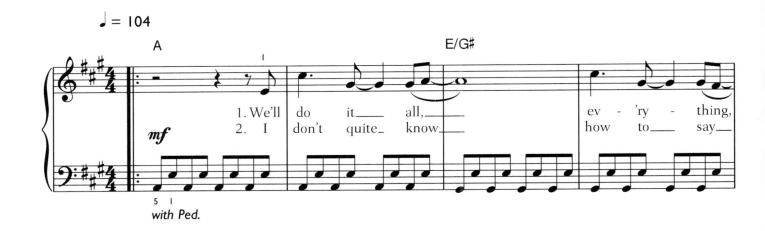

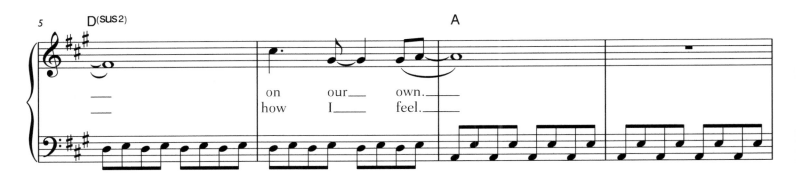

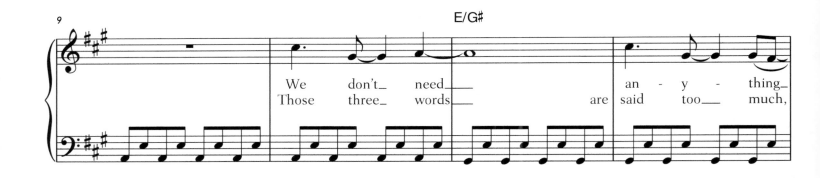

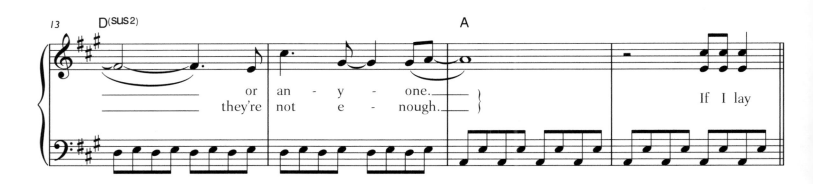

Bella's Lullaby
(from *Twilight*)

Composed by Carter Burwell

City Of Stars
(from *La La Land*)

Words by Benj Pasek and Justin Paul
Music by Justin Hurwitz

Cit - y of stars,— are you shin-ing just for me?—

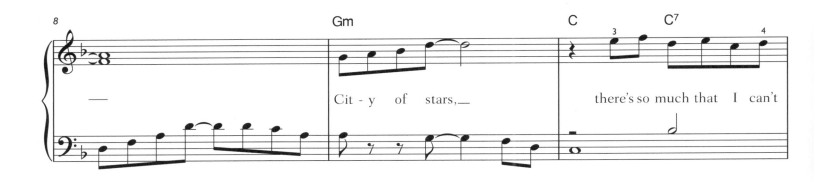

— Cit - y of stars,— there's so much that I can't

see.— Who knows?

No Surprises

Words and Music by Thomas Yorke, Jonathan Greenwood, Colin Greenwood, Edward O'Brien and Philip Selway

Not About Angels
(from the Motion Picture Soundtrack *The Fault In Our Stars*)

Words and Music by Jasmine van den Bogaerde

Walk Me Home

Words and Music by Alecia Moore, Scott Harris and Nate Ruess

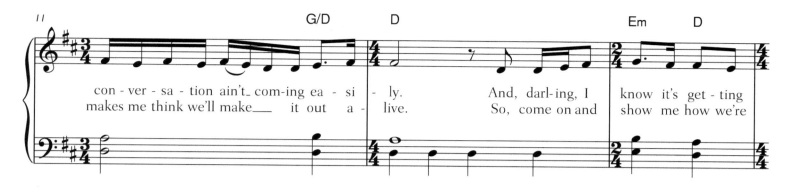

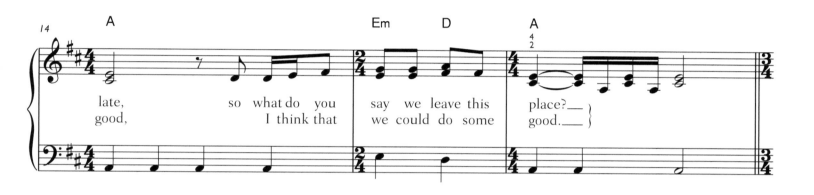

Dance Monkey

Words and Music by Toni Watson

I Will Always Love You

Words and Music by Dolly Parton

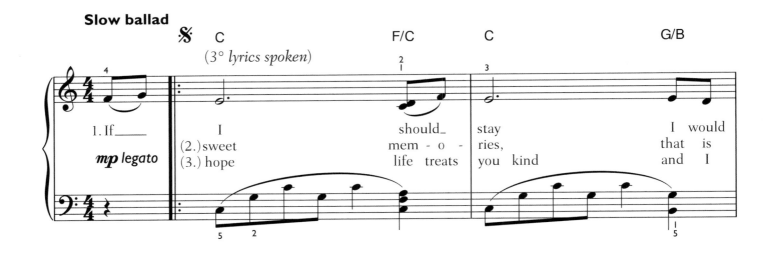

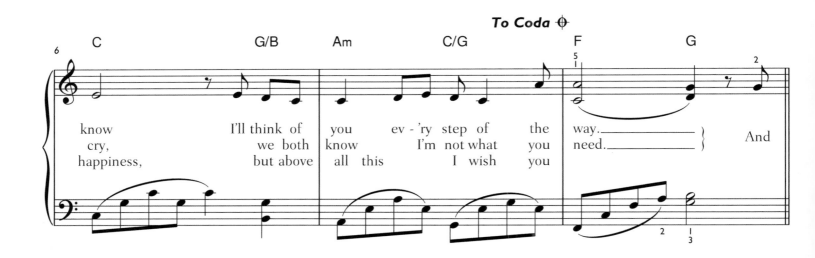

Your Song

Words and Music by Elton John and Bernie Taupin

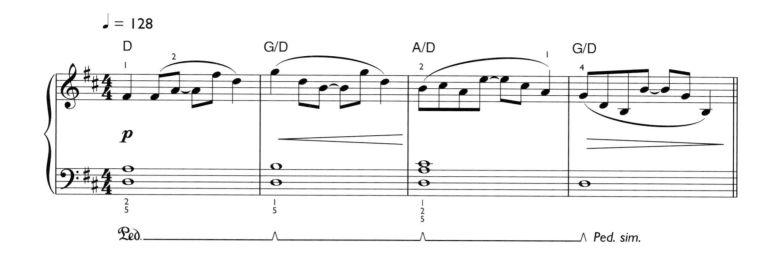

I hope you don't mind____ that I put____ down in words____

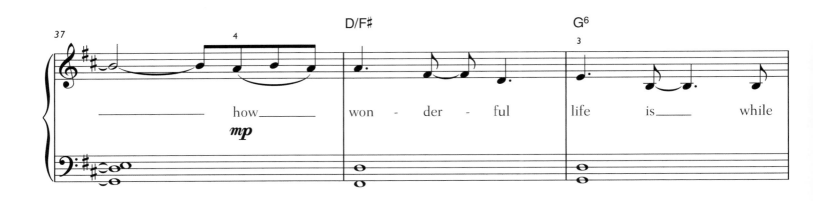

how_____ won - der - ful life is____ while

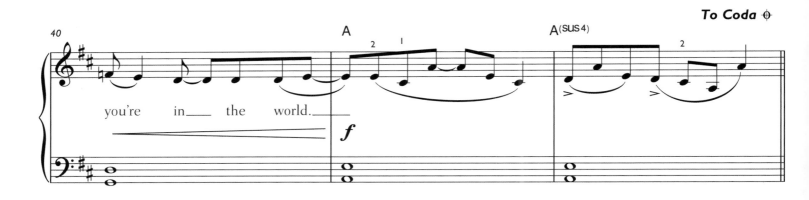

you're in____ the world.____

To Coda ⊕

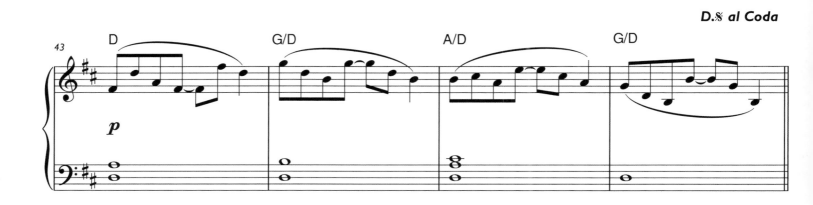

D.S al Coda

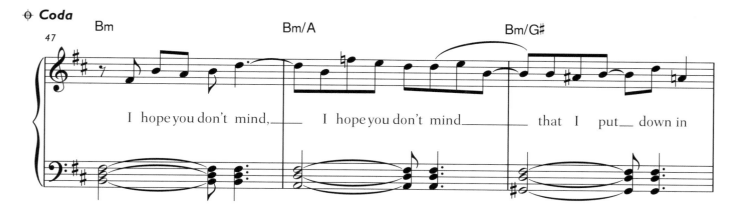

⊕ *Coda*

Bm   Bm/A   Bm/G#

I hope you don't mind,   I hope you don't mind   that I put down in

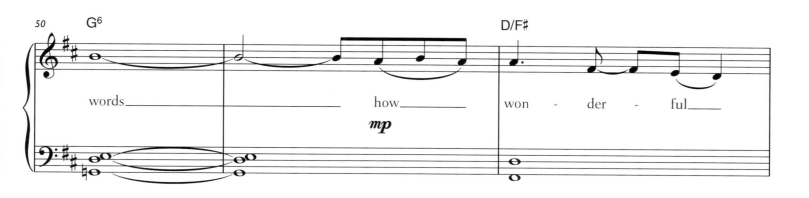

G⁶   D/F#

words   how   won - der - ful

mp

G⁶   D

life   is   while you're in the world.

G/D   A/D   G/D   D

f   *mf*

Prelude in A major

Composed by Frédéric Chopin

Love Me Like You Do

Words and Music by Max Martin, Savan Kotecha, Ilya, Ali Payami and Tove Lo

Love me like you do,   love, love, love me like you do,   love me like you do,   love, love,

love me like you do,   touch me like you do,   ta, ta, touch me like you do,____

____   what are you wait - ing for?____

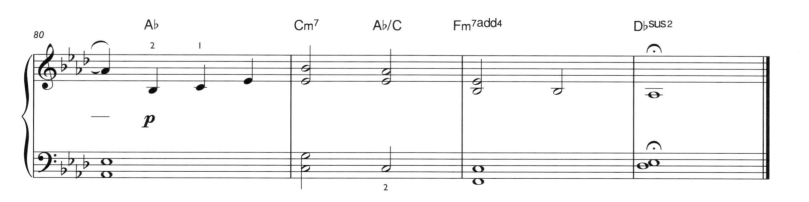

Tomorrow
(from *Annie*)

Words by Martin Charnin
Music by Charles Strouse

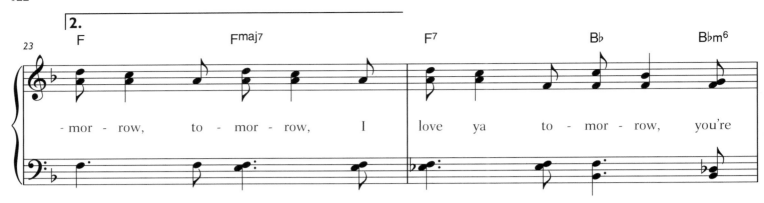

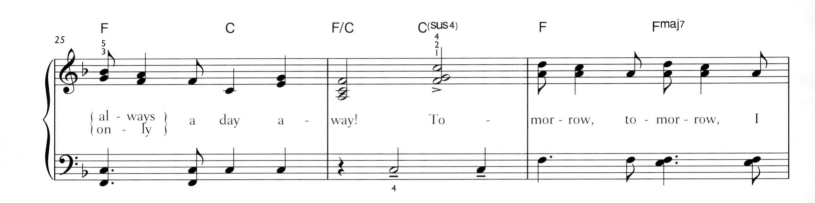

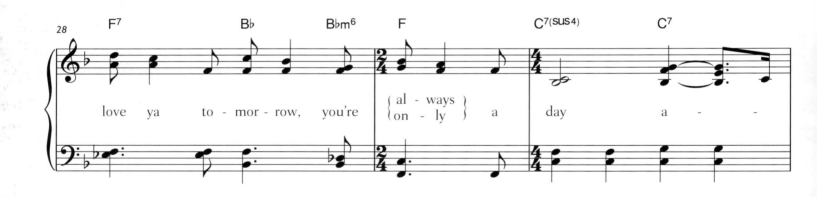

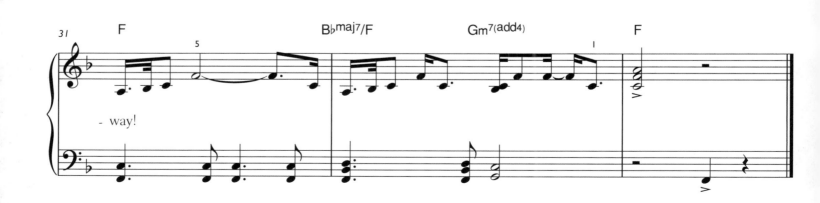

The Christmas Song (Chestnuts Roasting On An Open Fire)

Words and Music by Mel Tormé and Robert Wells

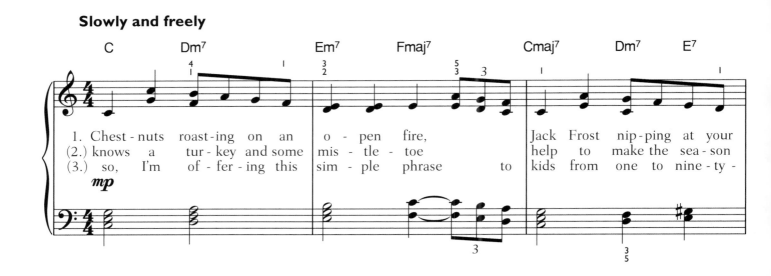

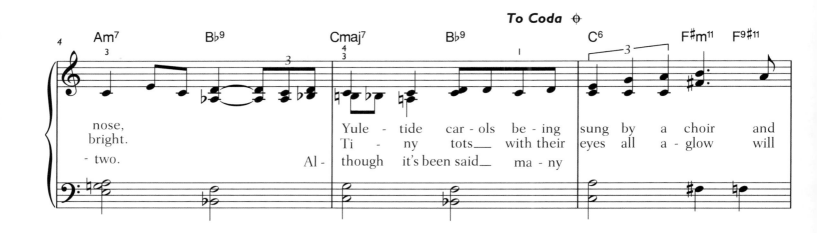

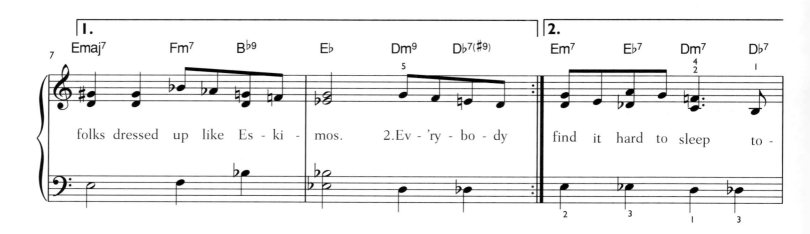

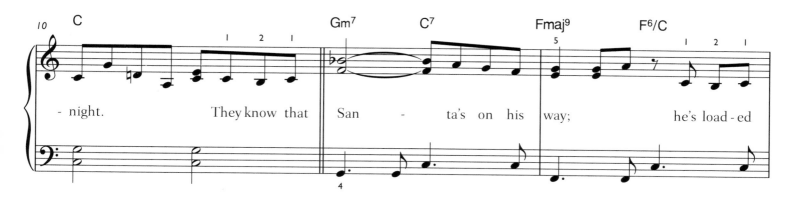

Ride

Words and Music by Tyler Joseph

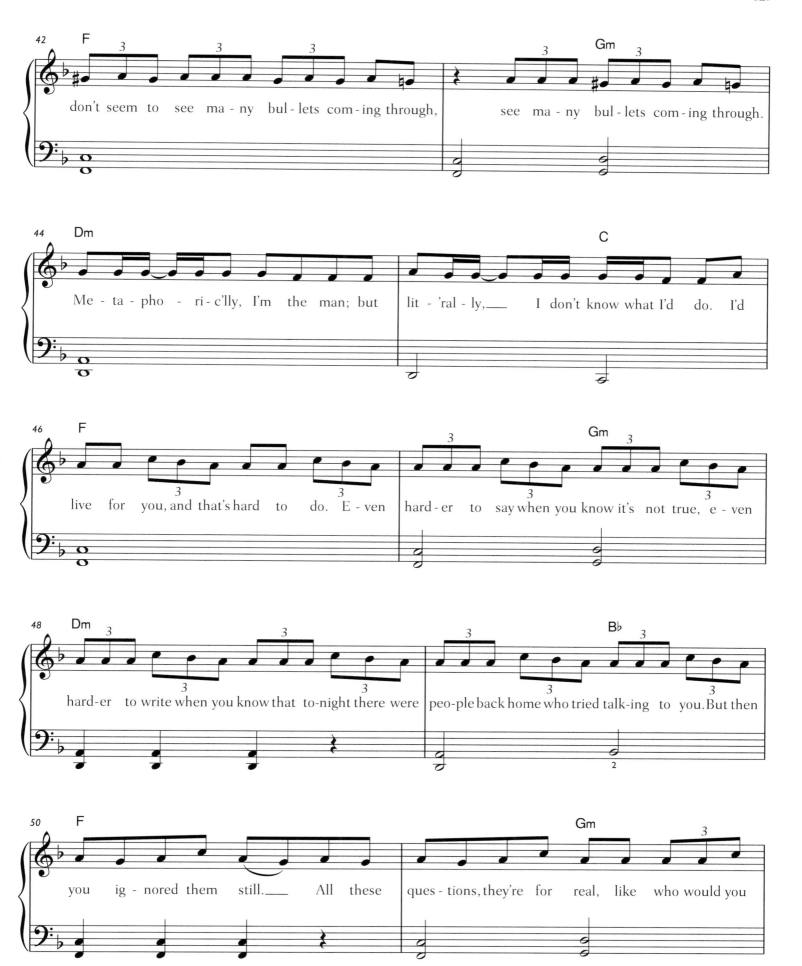

Cry Me A River

Words and Music by Arthur Hamilton

Feeling Good

Words and Music by Leslie Bricusse and Anthony Newley

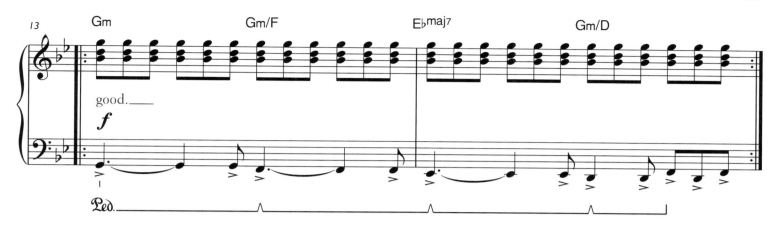

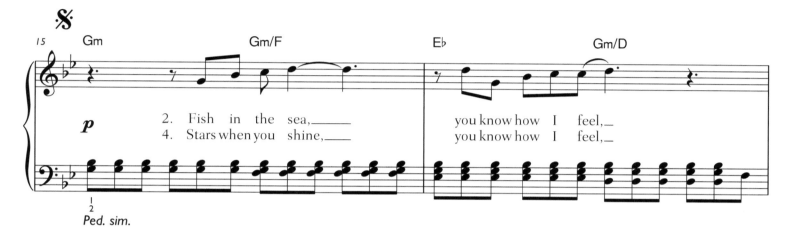

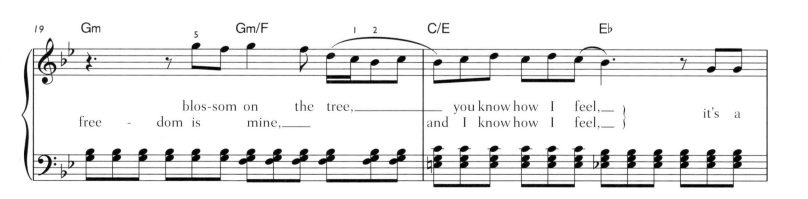

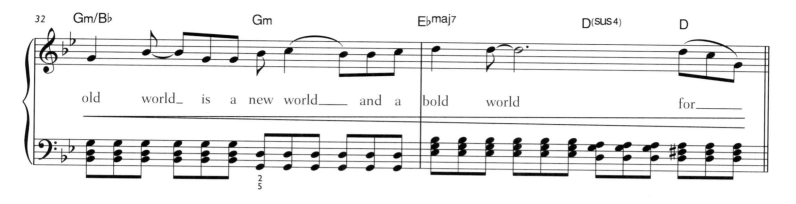

old world_ is a new world____ and a bold world for____

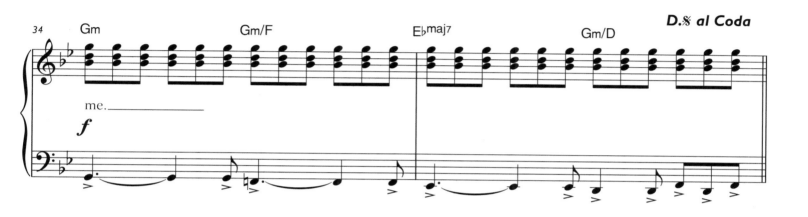

me.____

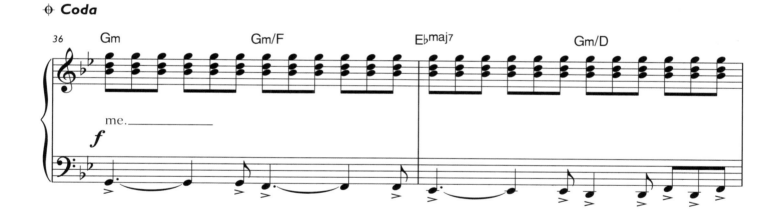

me.____

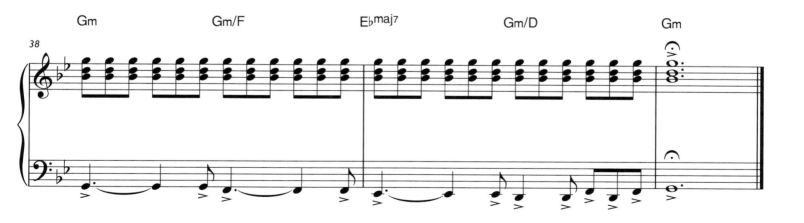

7 Years

Words and Music by Morten Ristorp Jensen, Lukas Forchhammer, Morten Pilegaard,
Don Stefano, David LaBrel and Chris "Brody" Brown

Soon I'll be six-ty years old, my dad-dy got six-ty - one, re-mem-ber life and then your

life be-comes a bet-ter one, I made a man so hap-py when I wrote a let-ter once,

I hope my child-ren come and vi - sit once or twice a month.

Soon I'll be six-ty years old, will I think the world is cold or will I have a lot of

child- ren who can warm me?_ Soon I'll be six - ty years old.

Soon I'll be six - ty years

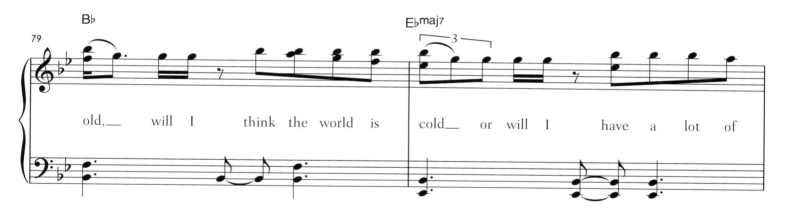

old,__ will I think the world is cold__ or will I have a lot of

child- ren who can warm me? Soon I'll be six - ty years old.

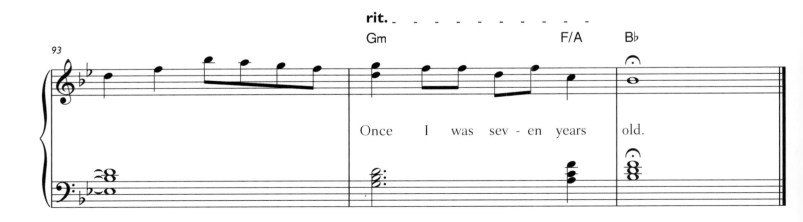

All I Ask

Words and Music by Adele Adkins, Philip Lawrence, Bruno Mars and Chris Brown

Scales And Arpeggios
(from *The Aristocats*)

Words and Music by Richard M. Sherman and Robert B. Sherman

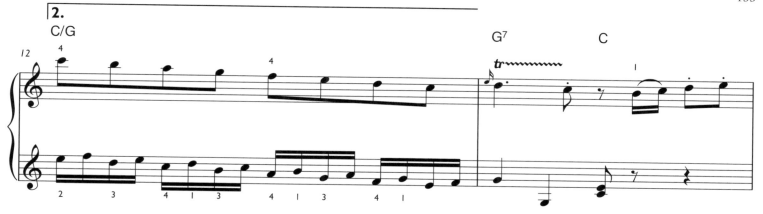

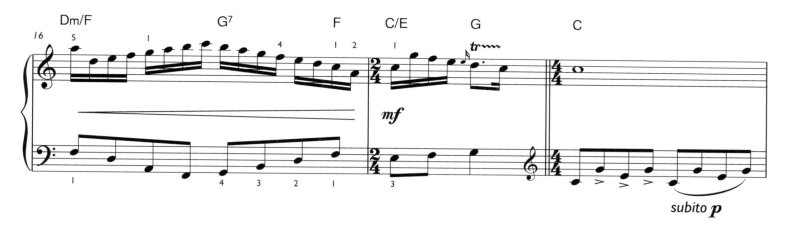

Moonlight Sonata
(Op.27, No.2)

Composed by Ludwig van Beethoven

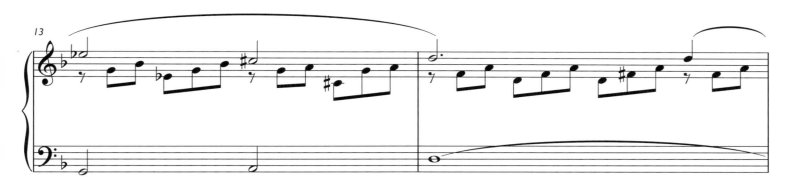

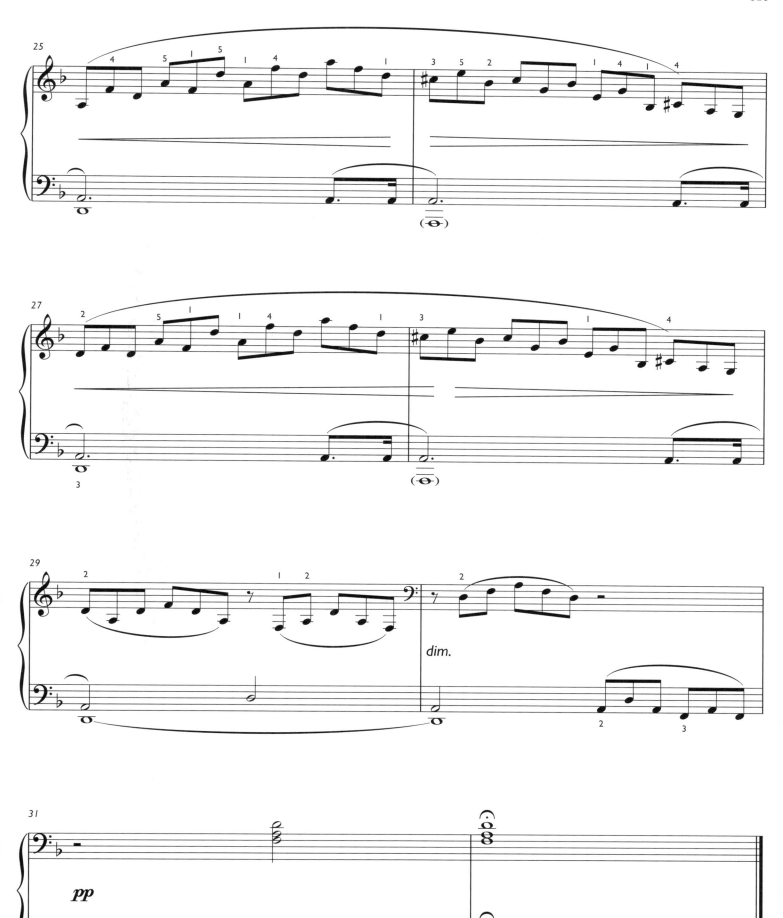

Pavane
(Op.50)

Composed by Gabriel Fauré

Hedwig's Theme
(from *Harry Potter And The Philosopher's Stone*)

Composed by John Williams

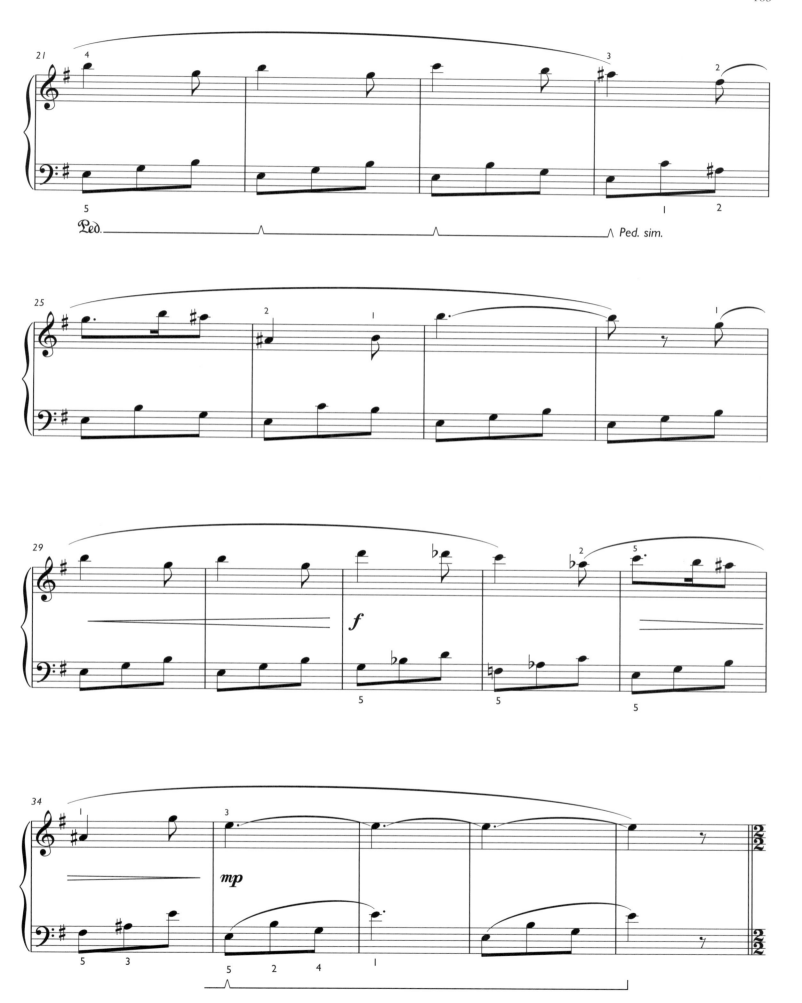

Brightly

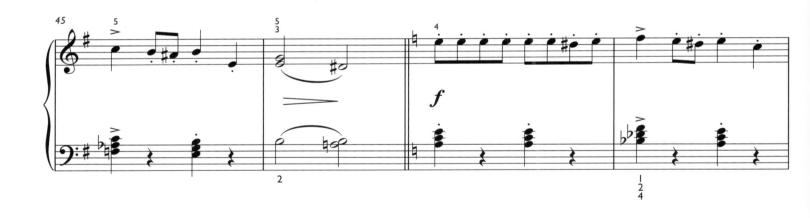

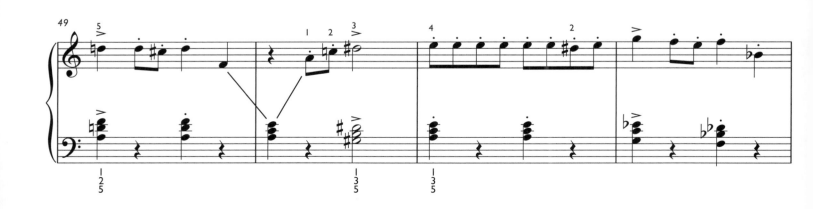

Sandcastles

Words and Music by Vincent Berry II, Midian Mathers, Malik Jones and Beyoncé Knowles

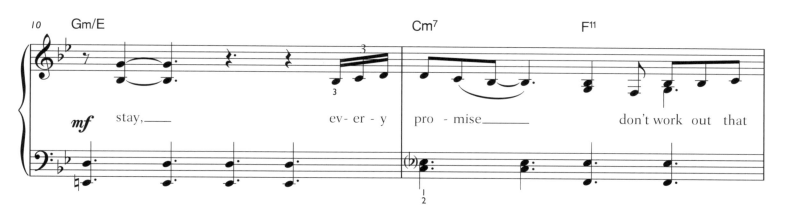

stay,____ ev-er-y pro-mise_____ don't work out that

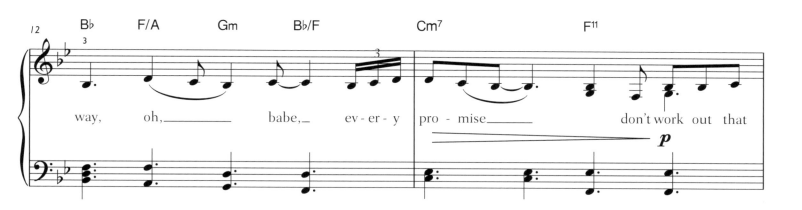

way, oh,_____ babe,_ ev-er-y pro-mise_____ don't work out that

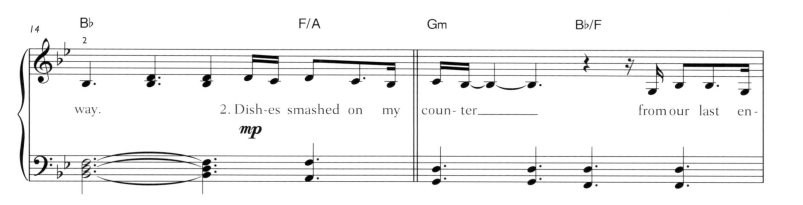

way. 2. Dish-es smashed on my coun-ter_____ from our last en-

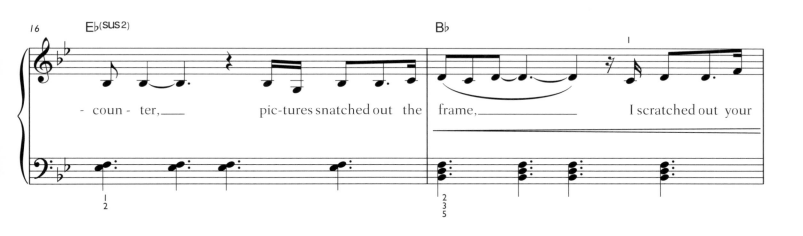

- coun-ter,__ pic-tures snatched out the frame,_____ I scratched out your

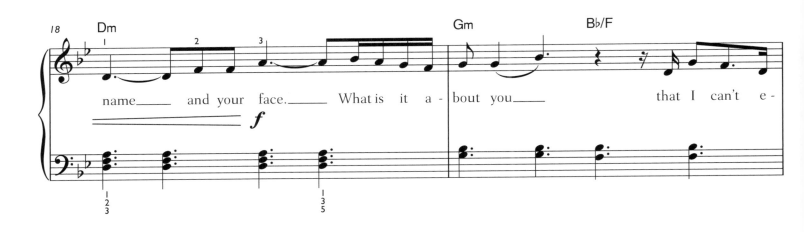

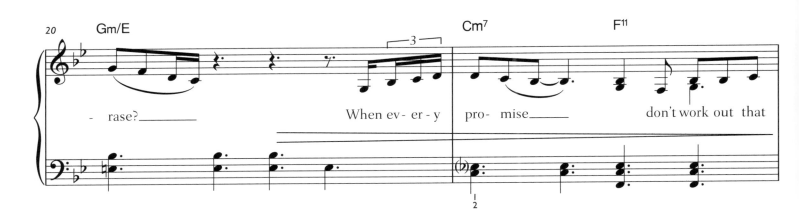

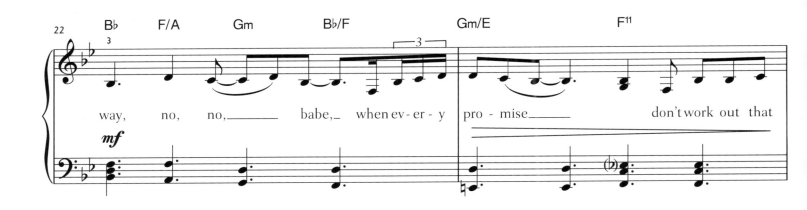

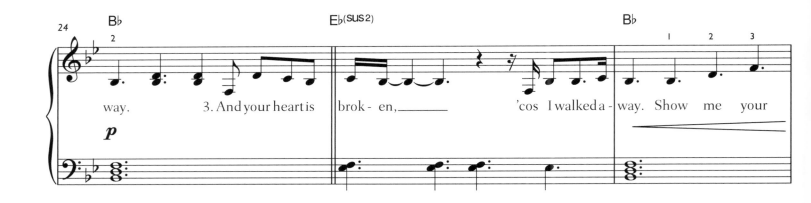

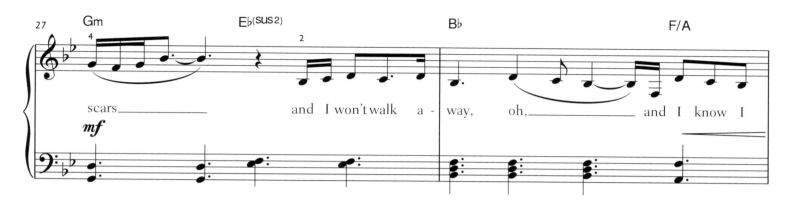

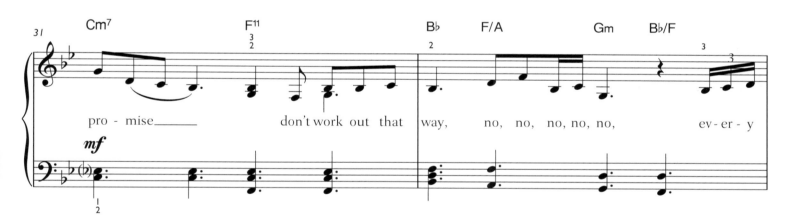

Thinking Out Loud

Words and Music by Ed Sheeran and Amy Wadge